This journal belongs to:

- -

Published in the UK by Scholastic Children's Books, 2020
Euston House, 24 Eversholt Street, London NW1 1DB
A division of Scholastic Limited

London ~ New York ~ Toronto ~ Sydney ~ Auckland
Mexico City ~ New Delhi ~ Hong Kong

SCHOLASTIC and associated logos are trademarks and/or
registered trademarks of Scholastic Inc.

© Scholastic Children's Books, 2020
Written by Emily Stead and designed by Cloud King Creative
Illustrations © Andrew Farley, 2020, and Shutterstock

ISBN 978 07023 0344 9

Printed in China

Papers used by Scholastic Children's Books are made from wood grown in sustainable forests.

2 4 6 8 10 9 7 5 3 1

www.scholastic.co.uk

Puppy Love
My Adorable Journal

Whether you already have a puppy or are
dreaming of your own pup, this journal is perfect
for planning all of your paw-some adventures together!
Start in any month you like, then fill the pages full of
puppy love, to create a journal to treasure for ever!

■SCHOLASTIC

My Puppy Owner Profile

Do you already own an adorable pup or
do you dream of getting one? Fill in these
pages about yourself and your perfect pet.

My name:

My age:

My birthday:

My favourite things:

My perfect pup

Pup's name: _____ boy 〇 girl 〇

Breed:

Fur colour: _____ Eye colour:

Personality in one word:

Cutest habit:

Cheekiest habit:

Draw or stick a photo of
you and your pup here!

January: a Pup's First Year

Looking after a puppy is a big job! Puppies need lots of love and care during their first year. Here's how to help your pup grow up into a happy and healthy dog.

The first few days

Pups need to be close to their mum to stay safe and warm. They will spend most of their time asleep or suckling their mum's milk. One of the first places you and your new puppy should go together is to the vet, to check that your pup is healthy.

The first few weeks

Choose a puppy crate or a cosy basket with a blanket for your pup, somewhere warm and quiet. Buy some toys for your pup to play with and get them used to wearing a collar. When your pup's baby teeth appear, they can have soft food alongside milk.

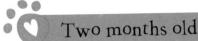

Two months old

This month is when puppies' adult teeth begin to come through, so hide anything away that you don't want to be chewed! Your puppy should receive their first vaccinations at around eight weeks.

Four months old

Once your pup has had all their vaccinations, they are ready to explore the outside world! Take your pup for walks and enrol them in puppy classes to help them learn basic training and meet new friends. The commands learned will help you play the fun games on pages 66–67.

One year old

Happy birthday! Most puppies are now becoming adult dogs, but remain playful and curious about the world. Pups still need lots of sleep and exercise at this age, as well as plenty of cuddles!

January: Adopt a Pup!

Choosing the perfect puppy name isn't easy,
so here's a helping paw! Imagine you were adopting
a new puppy, what would it be called?

First, look for the first letter of your first name...

A – Luna

B – Rover

C – Coco

D – Marley

E – Fluffball

F – Bentley

G – Scruff

H – Tails

I – Indie

J – Brownie

K – Pepper

L – Angel

M – Max

N – Scamp

O – Lucky

P – Patch

Q – Dotty

R – Woofy

S – Smudge

T – Bitsy

U – Sky

V – Cookie

W – Bailey

X – Scrappy

Y – Buttons

Z – Peanut

Now find the month in which you were born...

January – Puppins
February – Furdinand
March – Le Cute
April – Barks-a-Lot
May – Howler
June – Woofington

July – Wagglesworth
August – Proudpaws
September – the Furbulous
October – Kitty-Chaser
November – Barkley
December – McDoggins

Write your
pup's name here: ------------------------------

January

What did you do to celebrate
a brand-new year?

Week 1

- -

- -

- -

- -

Week 2

- -

- -

- -

- -

Week 3

- -

- -

- -

- -

Week 4

- -

- -

- -

- -

February: Puppy Facts

It's a fact – puppies are adorable! What else do you know about your favourite furry friends, though? Read on to discover some surprising puppy facts.

Puppies are born blind and deaf. They can't see or hear until they are almost two weeks old. Aww!

Just like humans, puppies are born without teeth and grow baby teeth that fall out. By the time they are six months old, pups should have a full set of adult teeth.

Dalmatian pups aren't born with their famous spots – the patches develop as the pups grow older.

Just like human fingerprints, no two dogs' nose prints are the same.

Pups in the same litter often look alike, but did you know that puppies can have identical twins? Cute!

Fur babies are more like human babies than you might think... both need lots of sleep when they are first born – between 15 and 20 hours. Night-night!

It is thought that the word 'puppy' comes from the French word 'poupée', which means 'doll'.

While the average number of puppies in a litter is between four and six, the record litter is 24 pups, born to a mummy Neopolitan Mastiff. Wow!

February: Puppy Puzzle

Let's play puppy hide-and-seek! Find 14 types of pup hiding in the grid. The names read forwards, up, down and diagonally.

PUG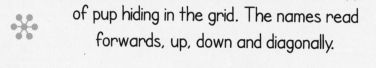

DALMATIAN

BULLDOG

POODLE

LABRADOR

DASCHUND

GERMAN SHEPHERD

SPANIEL

TERRIER

BEAGLE

JACK RUSSELL

POMERANIAN

HUSKY

CORGI

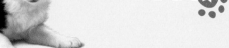

A word-search puzzle of dog breeds, with hidden words including BEAGLE, DACHSHUND, SPANIEL, POMERANIAN.

```
                                          C S C
                                          R U O L P
              O P                       T N C R N E U F
            L J                         R M Q D G G V H G
        V A R                           B O H G O I S I K
        H B
  D F R     R T V H J X O B S       P Z L U E E F T
  B E A G L E I D A S C H U N D I O H V L S R L E
  K L D T D R R M Q D B K S L Q D B K S E K M D A
  S K O P A R P R S P A N I E L B K S L S Y A O D
  V R E L I Q N I Q D B K S I D R M O S S N O L
  D H M E E B K E P A S A N I O C O U I S P R
  B S A R P O M E R A N I A N N G P R K H C D
  D N T L W V H J X Q D B K S D F P K S E S
    K I A N I                 Q C W P U
    T A E B                   E A N H R
    A N L                     J D E K
    J X A T                   R R N E
    W V I A                   E D D J
```

The answers are on page 78.

Which is your favourite pup? Write it here:

17

February

Write down some of your
favourite February memories.

Week 1

- -

- -

- -

- -

Week 2

- -

- -

- -

- -

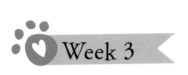 Week 3

 Week 4

19

March: Shopping List

Imagine that you were bringing a lovely puppy home. Unscramble the words below to make a shopping list of all the things that your new pup would need!

1. dofo _ _ _ _

2. elda _ _ _ _

3. shrbu _ _ _ _ _

4. kestab _ _ _ _ _ _

5 slowb   _ _ _ _ _

6 locarl   _ _ _ _ _ _

7 wech oty   _ _ _ _ _ _ _

8 kenlabt   _ _ _ _ _ _ _

9 albl   _ _ _ _

The answers are on page 78.

March:
Pick the Perfect Puppy

Take this fun quiz to find out which breed of puppy
could be just right for you and your family.

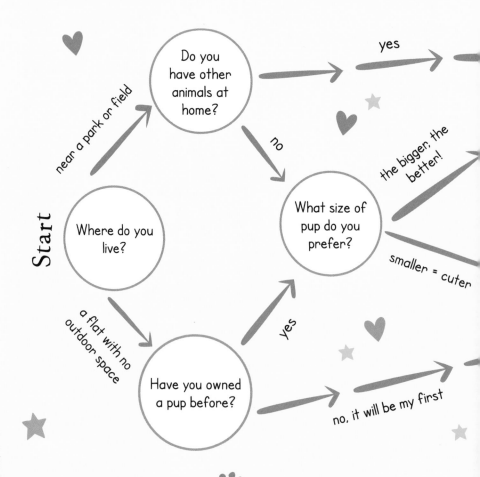

Start

near a park or field

Where do you live?

a flat with no outdoor space

Do you have other animals at home?

yes

no

Have you owned a pup before?

yes

no, it will be my first

What size of pup do you prefer?

the bigger, the better!

smaller = cuter

Do you like spending time outdoors?

yes, I love it!

Old English sheepdog
Large dogs like Old English sheepdogs need lots of exercise and space to run about. These friendly dogs will be kind to other pets.

yes, for short periods

Jack Russell
These noisy pups love to run and chase, so need an owner who can keep up with them! One or two walks a day will burn off their energy.

How much barking can you handle?

I don't mind a chatty pup!

I'd like a quieter pup, please!

French bulldog
A small, quiet dog like a bulldog that doesn't need long walks or lots of space could work for your family. French bulldogs love cuddles and are easy to train, too.

March

How did you spend your days
and weeks in March?

Week 1

Week 2

Week 3

Week 4

April: Puppy Party

It's paw-ty time! Why not plan a puppy-themed party
in celebration of your favourite furry friends?
Ask your pals to bring their soft toy pups, too.

Plan your menu.
What will you offer
your guests?

MENU

pupcorn

pupperoni pizza

mini hot dogs

paw-tato crisps

perfect pupcakes

My ideas: _____

_____

Now choose some
games to play:

pin the tail on the puppy pic ♡   puppy karaoke ♡

doggie dress-up ♡   fetch relay ♡

My ideas: _____

26

How about some doggie decorations to make everything look paw-fect?

My ideas: _____

_____

_____

_____

Copy this design or create your own party invitation. Take copies, then stick on to card to share with your friends.

You are invited to my puppy party!

Date: _____

Time: _____

Place: _____

RSVP to: _____

April: Paw-fect Pupcakes

A doggie treat that's so yummy to eat! Try making these cute cakes for people, not pups.

Ask an adult to help, if you get stuck.

You will need:
- icing sugar
- light brown fondant icing
- dark brown fondant icing
- a round biscuit cutter
- 6 shop-bought fairy cakes
- black fondant icing
- a cocktail stick
- a black cake-decorating pen
- buttercream or jam

1 Dust your chopping board with icing sugar.

2 Knead the light brown fondant icing to soften, then roll it out until it is about 1/2 cm thick.

3 Find a round cutter that is the same size as your fairy cakes. Cut out a topper for each cake, or ask an adult to help you.

4 Make a small muzzle shape then two floppy ears using the dark brown icing. Stick in place using a little water.

5 Make two small balls for eyes and a little triangle nose using the black icing, then stick in place.

6 Use a cocktail stick to make tiny holes on the muzzle. Draw a mouth with the decorating pen.

7 Use buttercream or jam to attach a topper to each cake, then your first pupcake is ready! Repeat for each cake.

Simply paw-fect!

April

What were some of your favourite activities in April?

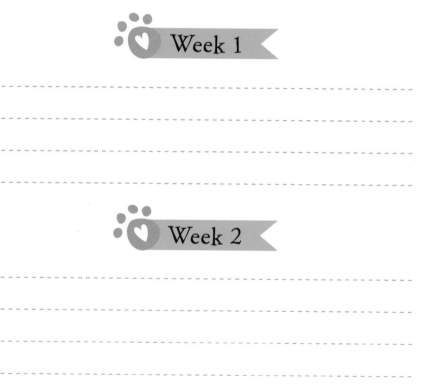

Week 1

Week 2

Week 3

- -

- -

- -

- -

Week 4

- -

- -

- -

- -

May: Pups in Books

There are plenty of tales where pups are the stars!
How many of the famous dogs below have you read about?

Dogger

Shirley Hughes' Dogger is a cuddly toy
dog that belongs to a little boy called
Dave. One day, though, something
terrible happens – Dave loses Dogger!
Will Dogger and Dave ever be reunited?

Spot

A playful pup created by Eric Hill who is
loved by toddlers everywhere! Spot loves to
play hide-and-seek with his mum, Sally, and
discover the world when it's time for walkies.

101 Dalmatians

The heroes of a Disney film based on
Dodie Smith's book, parents Pongo and
Perdita must leap to the rescue when
their adorable spotty pups are stolen
by the villainous Cruella de Vil.

Snowy

Snowy is Tintin's terrier companion in Hergé's The Adventures of Tintin series. The pair travel everywhere together, with Snowy often keeping his detective pal safe from danger.

Dog Man

Dog Man is a series of books by Dav Pilkey that will have you howling with laughter! Its hero is a cartoon part-dog, part-human police officer who has a talent for sniffing out crime.

Winn-Dixie

The scruffy star of the classic story *Because of Winn-Dixie*, this pup is named after an American supermarket chain! Kate Di Camillo's summer tale is both funny and warm.

Puppy fact
Did you know that some schools and libraries have special reading dogs that help children learn to read?

May: a Pup's Tale

Write down a word for each of the categories listed below.
Then copy the words into the spaces on the next page.
Once you have finished, read your puppy tale out loud!

1. An action _____

2. A describing word _____

3. A part of the pup's body _____

4. A describing word _____

5. A part of the pup's body _____

6. A describing word _____

7. A pup's name _____

8. A puppy action _____

9. A puppy action _____

10. Some spoken words _____

11. Somewhere a pup sleeps _____

Exciting news! A new puppy was going to come and live with us! I promised I would look after it and always

1. _____ . When it arrived, it was so

2. _____ ! Its 3. _____ was

4. _____ and its 5. _____ was so

6. _____ . I named it 7. _____ .

Our favourite things to do together were 8. _____

_____ and 9. _____ . We soon

became best friends! Every night at bedtime, I would say:

10. "_____ !" before

my pup fell fast asleep in 11. _____ .

May

What special memories did you make in May?

Week 1

Week 2

Week 3

Week 4

June: Do You Speak Dog?

Have you ever wondered what all those woofs, whines and whimpers really mean? Try these tips to communicate with your pup to gain their trust and become best buddies!

Making friends

People can seem like giants when towering over tiny pups. Crouching down at your pup's level will make them feel less nervous.

Hold out your hand with an open palm, then let your puppy greet you with a friendly sniff.

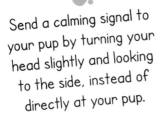

Send a calming signal to your pup by turning your head slightly and looking to the side, instead of directly at your pup.

Train your pup by repeating the same simple commands each time, 'sit' or 'down'. When your pup does the action, reward them with a healthy treat.

Noisy pups!

Barking: a barking pup has something to tell you! Is there someone at the door? Do they want to play? Listen carefully to your pup's barks and try not to shout – it may cause them to bark more.

Whining: pups often whine when they want something. Your pup might be trying to tell you that they are ready for a walk ... or their dinner!

Whimpering: a whimpering pup can mean they are in pain or not feeling well. If the whimpers won't go away, try a trip to the vet.

June

What amazing adventures
did you have in June?

 Week 1

Week 2

Week 3

- -

- -

- -

- -

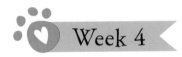
Week 4

- -

- -

- -

- -

July: Meet the Pups!

There are hundreds of different breeds of dog,
and just like you, each pup has its own personality.
Take a look at some puppy profiles below.

Cavalier King Charles spaniel

Personality: friendly, easy to train, gentle
Coat: chestnut, white, black, tan, ruby
Size: small
Puppy fact: these gorgeous pups love
company and will follow you everywhere you go.

French bulldog

Personality: affectionate, alert, playful
Coat: fawn, black, white
Size: small
Puppy fact: these pooches make cute companions!
They love to play...and snooze!

Beagle

Personality: lively, friendly, trusting
Coat: black, tan, white, red
Size: small to medium
Puppy fact: super-friendly pups that love long walks. They make excellent sniffer dogs, too.

Cocker spaniel

Personality: happy, playful, sporty
Coat: black, brown, red, golden
Size: small
Puppy fact: Cocker spaniels are a happy breed. They love walks and like to make themselves heard!

German shepherd

Personality: obedient, clever, hardworking
Coat: black, grey, tan
Size: large
Puppy fact: German shepherds make brave police dogs. They can also be assistance dogs, helping people with disabilities, as well as loyal family pets.

July: How to Draw a Pug

Follow these simple steps to draw
a super-cuddly pug.

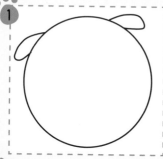

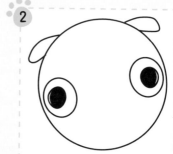

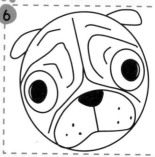

Use this space to sketch out your pretty pug.

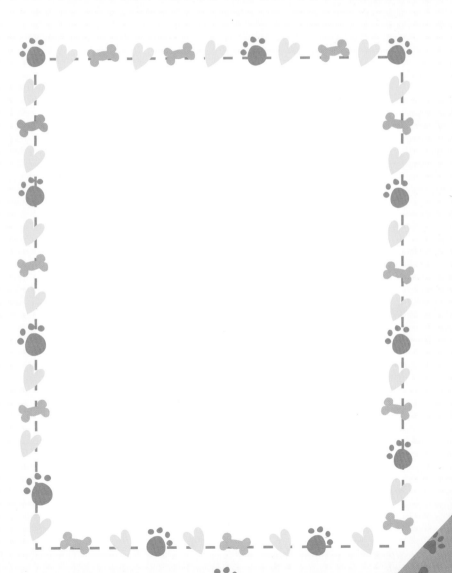

July

What made your July
a happy month?

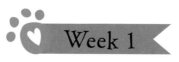

Week 1

Week 2

Week 3

Week 4

August: Puppy Postcards

Brighten up someone's day by sharing all your
paw-some news on a puppy postcard!
There are two different designs to send.

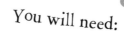
You will need:

- safety scissors
- glue stick
- card
- pen or pencil

An adult
should be
close by when
scissors are
in use.

1 Carefully cut out
the postcards on
the next page. You could
stick them on to card.

2 Write a message
to another pup-lover
or someone in your family
telling them all about your
puppy adventures!

3 Write your message
on the left-hand side
and the person's address
on the right-hand side.

4 Use the space below
to spell out any long
words first or to think
of ideas.

August: Puppy Close-ups

Look carefully. Which little detail belongs to the pups in the big pictures? Draw lines to make a match.

The answers are on page 78.

1

2

3

Border collie

German shepherd

Jack Russell

August

Write about some of the fun
activities that made your August great!

Week 1

Week 2

Week 3

Week 4

September: Puppy Poem

Try your paw at writing a special poem
all about your real or dream pup.

An acrostic poem starts with a vertical word,
then uses each letter of that word to begin
a line of the poem. For example:

C urly-haired

O bedient

O ften asleep

K ind and friendly

I nto everything!

E ats a lot

Puppy tip
Each line can be
a single word or a
longer sentence.
It's up to you!

Now it's your turn... write out your pup's name below, using a new line for each letter. Then write a line for each letter that perfectly describes your pup!

September: Puppy Parlour

Show your pup just how much you love them with
a trip to the puppy parlour! Which treatments
will you choose to pamper your pet?

Puppy pamper list:

🐾 bath and shampoo 🤍

🐾 groom and blow-dry 🤍

🐾 fur trim 🤍

🐾 paw-dicure 🤍

🐾 teeth cleaning 🤍

🐾 spa treat 🤍

Now draw your pup looking all groomed and gorgeous!

September

What did you enjoy doing most
in the month of September?

Week 1

Week 2

Week 3

Week 4

October: Doggie Door Hanger

Make this fun door hanger to let friends and family know when you and your pup are ready to play ... or when you need some quiet time.

1 Carefully cut out the page along the blue vertical dotted line.

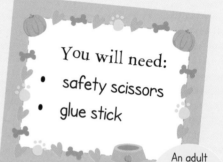

You will need:
- safety scissors
- glue stick

An adult should be close by when scissors are in use.

2 Now carefully cut around the door hanger shape.

Shhh!
Pups sleeping!

Pups at play!
Come on in!

3 Glue around the edges of one side of the hanger and fold the sides together.

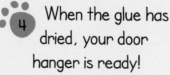

4 When the glue has dried, your door hanger is ready!

Shhh!

Pups sleeping!

Pups at play!

Come on in!

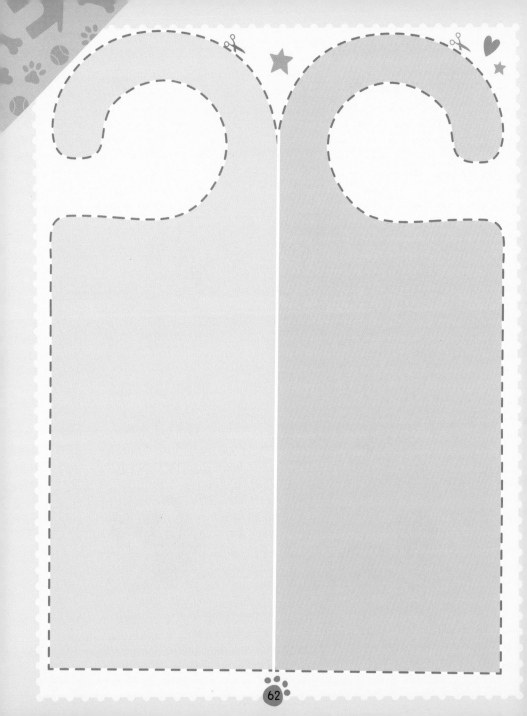

October: Odd Dog Out

Which of these dotty Dalmatians looks different from the rest? Circle the odd dog out.

The answers are on page 78.

October

Write about some of your
favourite October memories below!

Week 1

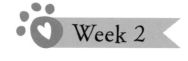
Week 2

 Week 3

- -

- -

- -

- -

Week 4

- -

- -

- -

- -

November: Fun and Games

Puppies love to play! Keep your pup busy and have fun together by trying some of these fun games. Remember to let your pup win sometimes to boost their confidence.

Fetch

Choose a soft toy or ball that your pup can't swallow. Ask them to 'sit' or 'stay', then throw the toy a short distance away. Say 'fetch' and ask them to 'drop it' at your feet. As lots of commands are used here, be patient with your pup!

Fun rating:

☆ ☆ ☆ ☆ ☆

Flying disc

This game is best played with larger pups! Find a dog-friendly disc that will be gentle on your pup's teeth and gums, then test out their aerial acrobatics as the disc flies through the air!

Fun rating:

☆ ☆ ☆ ☆ ☆

Tug of war

Use a rope toy to play a tug of war game and teach commands like 'take it' and 'drop it'. Remember not to pull too hard, as puppy teeth are just developing.

Fun rating:

☆ ☆ ☆ ☆ ☆

Bubble chase

Chasing bubbles is always a pup-ular game! Blow non-toxic bubbles (or special pup-friendly ones) for your pup to pop. Remember to wipe your dog's face at the end of the game.

Fun rating:

☆ ☆ ☆ ☆ ☆

Hide-and-seek

This game lets your dog use some of their natural scent-tracking abilities in a fun way. Tell your pup to 'stay' while you find a hiding place. Then call your pup and make a fuss of them when they find you!

Fun rating:

☆ ☆ ☆ ☆ ☆

Puppy tip
Use the same commands that your pup learned in training.

My ideas: _____

_____

November: Puppy Jokes

Read these daft doggy jokes that will have you howling with laughter! Then think of a joke of your own.

Q: Why should you take care when it rains cats and dogs?

A: Because you might step in a poodle!

Q: Why can't pups work the TV remote?

A: Because they always hit the paws button!

Q: What is a dog's favourite sweet treat?

A: Pupcakes!

Q: What do you get when you cross a dog with a phone?

A: A golden receiver!

Q: Why did the Dalmatian go to the optician?
A: He kept seeing spots!

Q: Which breed of pup is the funniest?
A: A chi-ha-ha!

Q: What did one flea say to the other?
A: Should we walk or take the dog?

Q: What is a dog's favourite pizza topping?
A: Pupperoni!

Q: What do you get when you cross
   a frog and a dog?
A: A croaker spaniel!

My joke:

Q: _____

A: _____

November

What made your November
a special month?

Week 1

_____

_____

_____

_____

Week 2

_____

_____

_____

_____

Week 3

- -

- -

- -

- -

Week 4

- -

- -

- -

- -

December:
Making Memories

What a year you've had! Write down some special puppy
memories here, so you will always remember them.

Something I'm proud of: ------------------------------------

Something unexpected that happened: -----------------------

My favourite moment of the year: --------------------------

Use this space to draw your dream pup
or stick in a special selfie of you
and your pup together!

December: Puppy Portraits

Read the descriptions, then fill the four frames with perfect puppy pictures!

A pup performing a clever trick.

A snuggly puppy, having a snooze.

A hungry pup enjoying a treat.

A mucky pup, just back from a walk.

December

What festive activities did you
enjoy doing in December?

Week 1

hzipzorer

Week 2

Week 3

Pip ꞁ

Week 4

Answers

Page 17

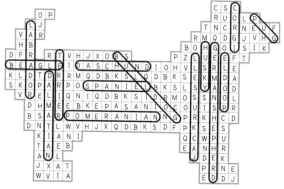

Pages 20–21

1. food, 2. lead, 3. brush, 4. basket, 5. bowls,
6. collar, 7. chew toy, 8. blanket, 9. ball.

Page 51

1. German shepherd, 2. Jack Russell, 3. Border collie.

Page 63

Puppy 4 is the odd one out.

Picture credits

Andrew Farley illustrations: 5, 6t, 6c, 9t, 11t, 11b, 14b, 15, 16, 17, 20, 21, 23t, 23c, 23b, 26, 27t, 27bl, 27bc, 27br, 28, 29bl, 30, 32, 35, 36, 38tl, 38tr, 39br, 40, 42t, 42b, 43t, 43c, 43b, 49t, 49b, 51t, 51b, 52, 58, 61tr, 61bl, 61br, 63, 63, 66t, 66b, 68, 69, 72, 73.
Shutterstock: Tanya Zima 12, 14t, 18, 24t, 46t, 56, 61tl, 66t, 74t, 74b, 76t.